OL' 556

Alaska's Mighty Steam Engine

Shannon Cartwright

Printed by Everbest Printing Co., Ltd., Nansha, China.

Library of Congress Control Number: 2006910867
10 9 8 7 6 5 4 3 2 1

Published by:
Shannon
5763 Glacier Highway
Juneau, AK 99801
www.takugraphics.com

The event in this story is fiction, but everything else is true; the Ol' 556 was one of two steam locomotives kept on standby for many years to pull diesel trains through floods at Nenana and elsewhere. The Susitna River is known for its dramatic ice break-ups that have flooded the rails and taken out bridges in the past. The blocks of ice are sometimes as long as a locomotive and more than eight feet thick.

Concrete ties are starting to replace the old wooden ones. Concrete can last up to 100 years—twice as long as the wooden ties. There are 3,300 ties per mile on the Alaska Railroad.

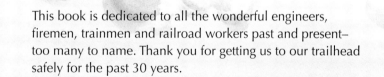

This book is dedicated to all the wonderful engineers, firemen, trainmen and railroad workers past and present– too many to name. Thank you for getting us to our trailhead safely for the past 30 years.

Thank you to everyone who helped me envision the Alaska Railroad's past: Weaver Franklin, Stuart White, Bob Barnett, Don Barnett, Keith Christensen, and to Pat Durand and Bob Yost, my Alaska Railroad facts experts.

A special thank you to Bill Spencer, Ann, David and Nowelle for your great editing to my story. And thank you to Shoo Salasky, Barb Totten, Edward Bovy and Mike Larsen for their production assistance.

Reference photo credit: Pat Durand's private collection and the collection of the Museum of Alaska Transportation and Industry.

—SC

Soon the familiar click-clack sound of the train rolling from section to section of rail will be gone. The lengths of rail are now being welded together creating one continuous welded rail.

Alaska's Railroads, Past and Present

The first railroad in the U.S. was built in 1827 in Massachusetts. It provided a cheaper, faster way to move freight than did teams of horses. By 1869, railroads connected the east coast with the west coast. They helped build our nation and remained the main form of transportation until the late 1940s.

Railroads reached their peak between 1941–1945 moving troops and army supplies. After World War II, railroads came into hard times when both highway and air travel became more available. Railroad construction began much later in Alaska.

In the early 1900s several railroads were built branching out from the **Nome** area—all going to nearby gold mines. Spongy tundra and drifting snow were major problems. The railroads declined as mining declined.

The Tanana Valley Railroad, 45 miles long, was built to serve Fairbanks and the nearby mining camps. Cold temperatures and drifting snow could close the railroad for weeks. Passengers sometimes had to be rescued by dog team. This railroad went bankrupt in 1917.

The **Copper River and Northwestern Railroad** was completed in 1911. It began in Cordova, crossed the Copper River, the faces of two glaciers, 8 miles of bridges and ended at the Kennecott Copper mines. Due to the decline in mining, the last train ran in 1939.

The **White Pass and Yukon Railway**, built during the Klondike gold rush, was completed in 1900. Its 111 miles connected Skagway, on the Alaska Coast, to Whitehorse, in the Yukon Territory. It carried miners and supplies to the interior and brought the gold out.

It was one of the most difficult railroads ever built because it climbs 2,900 feet in 21 miles. Most of the track was laid through solid rock that had been blasted and drilled by hand. A decline in mining closed the railway in 1982 but today the 20 miles between Skagway and White Pass Summit (the most scenic and historic portion of the line) are kept open as a tourist attraction.

Map ©Kalmbach Publishing Co.,
used with permission

The Alaska Railroad

Curry Hotel

The **Alaska Railroad** (ARR) was not the first railroad in Alaska, but it is the most influential and long lasting.

In the early days, the tourists came up by ship to Seward and Anchorage. The two main attractions were Denali (Mount McKinley) National Park at ARR mile 347.9 and the Curry Hotel at ARR mile 248.5.

The Curry Hotel was Alaska's most luxurious hotel from 1923 through the mid 1950s. It had a pool, golf course, ski tow, bakery, creamery, greenhouse, tennis courts and a suspension bridge across the Susitna River. This wilderness hotel burned down in 1957.

The railroad, now owned by the State of Alaska, starts at the Port of Seward, Mile 0 and ends in Fairbanks 470 miles north.

Construction started in 1915 and was completed in 1923. Early work gangs traveled by dog teams, packhorses and Caterpillar-like tractors. They built the railroad in sections; every 6-to 8 miles their camps became section stations where crews lived and maintained their part of the track. "Track walkers" checked their section daily.

Gradually most of the sections were closed with the introduction of more modern equipment for travel and maintenance. In the early days there were approximately 75 section stations with work crews. Now only a few section houses remain.

Today, the railroad transports everything from logs, gravel, coal, petroleum products, heavy equipment and passengers (numbering more than a half million, most of which are summer tourists) .

Some of the early steam engines operating in Alaska had big, ballooned smokestacks that helped trap and cool down hot sparks and cinders from the wood or coal burning fires.

The Alaska Railroad has been important in the 'opening up' of Alaska. Anchorage, Alaska's largest city, and many other Alaska towns started out as work camps along the rail. The ARR is the last full service railroad in the country offering both passenger and freight service year round. The ARR also operates the only local train in North America which still makes flag stops. It will pick up or drop off people at remote sites along the line.

In the early days when Alaska was wild and new, there were few roads in this northland. Mighty steam trains carried travelers into the wilderness and back out again. "All aboard" called the conductor, as miners, trappers, tourists, mushers, hunters, storekeepers and hardy homesteaders crowded the platform for the journey north.

Coal and water powered the black locomotives—
94 tons of hissing steam and smooth rolling steel.
Coal fed the fires... that boiled the water... to make
the steam... that built the pressure... that pushed
the pistons... that turned the big driving wheels.

Across the wild land the steam trains roamed,
stopping at section houses along the line to take
on coal and water to satisfy their huge appetite.

OL' 556

TENDER

In one day, just traveling 120 miles, the
No. 556 could burn 10,000 pounds of
coal, all of which was shoveled into
the firebox by the fireman! The engine
would also consume an average of
15,000 gallons of water a day, which
meant stopping three or four times to
top off its 6,500-gallon tank.

These amounts varied depending on
weather conditions, the train's load, the
track grade and the engineer. The early
steam engines, including the Ol' 556,
were "hand bombers", engines fired by
hand. The later steam engines were
equipped with "stokers" which had a
steam driven screw that fed coal into
the fire.

Light

Coupler

Coal capacity
14 tons

Water capacity
6500 gallons

Coal, water and sand were available at different section stations along the line.
There was a designated place for the fireman to deposit the ashes at all the water stops.

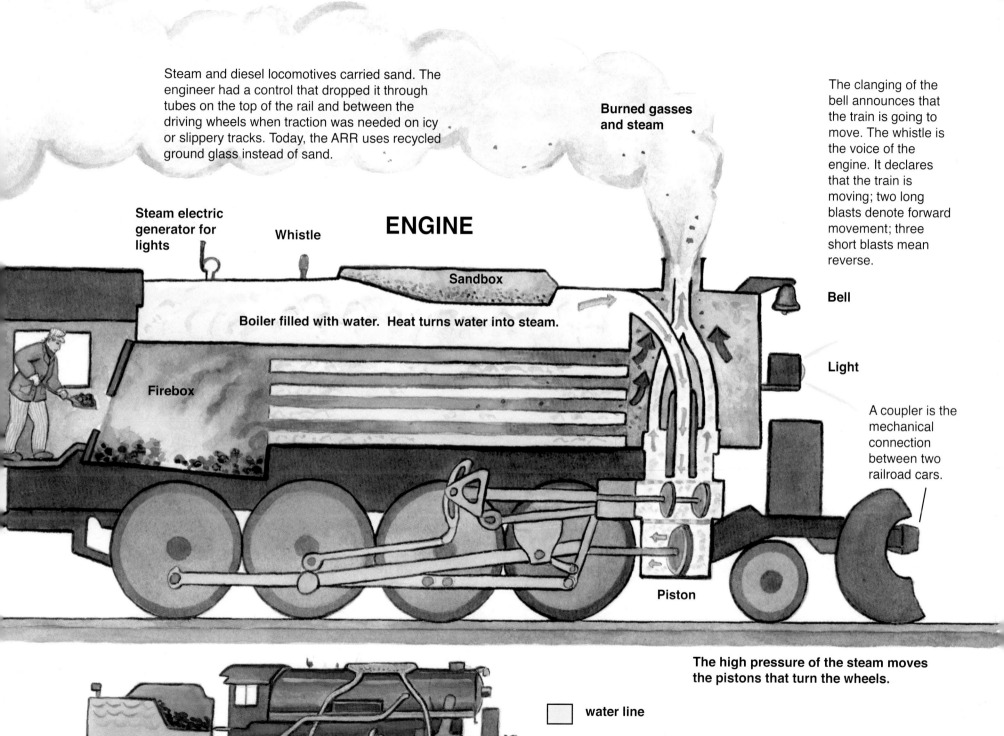

Steam and diesel locomotives carried sand. The engineer had a control that dropped it through tubes on the top of the rail and between the driving wheels when traction was needed on icy or slippery tracks. Today, the ARR uses recycled ground glass instead of sand.

Burned gasses and steam

The clanging of the bell announces that the train is going to move. The whistle is the voice of the engine. It declares that the train is moving; two long blasts denote forward movement; three short blasts mean reverse.

Steam electric generator for lights

Whistle

ENGINE

Sandbox

Bell

Boiler filled with water. Heat turns water into steam.

Light

Firebox

A coupler is the mechanical connection between two railroad cars.

Piston

The high pressure of the steam moves the pistons that turn the wheels.

water line

sand line

9

Clang! Clang! went the bell. WuuOO! WuuOO! went the whistle. Chisss! Chisss! went the valves. Chuuug... chuug... chug went the engine. Smoke and steam poured from the smokestack and billowed far behind as the trains rolled over mountain passes, across wide rivers and past glaciers as blue as the sky.

This was a lonesome land; few people heard the steam trains go by. But the wild critters that lived there did... bear, moose, sheep, wolves and caribou. They knew the familiar voice of Ol' 556 and barely looked up as their friend chugged past in a cloud of smoke and steam.

To overcome a steep grade and miss a glacier 50 miles north of Seward, the tracks formed a loop, circling around and over itself on a 100-foot high wooden trestle. With age, the high trestle sagged and would sway in the wind making for a very thrilling ride! "The Loop," which included five bridges, a snow shed and a tunnel was bypassed in 1951. The wooden bridges were too costly to keep maintained.

Drums of water were kept on each side of the wooden bridges along the railroad in case errant sparks from the steam engines set them on fire.

11

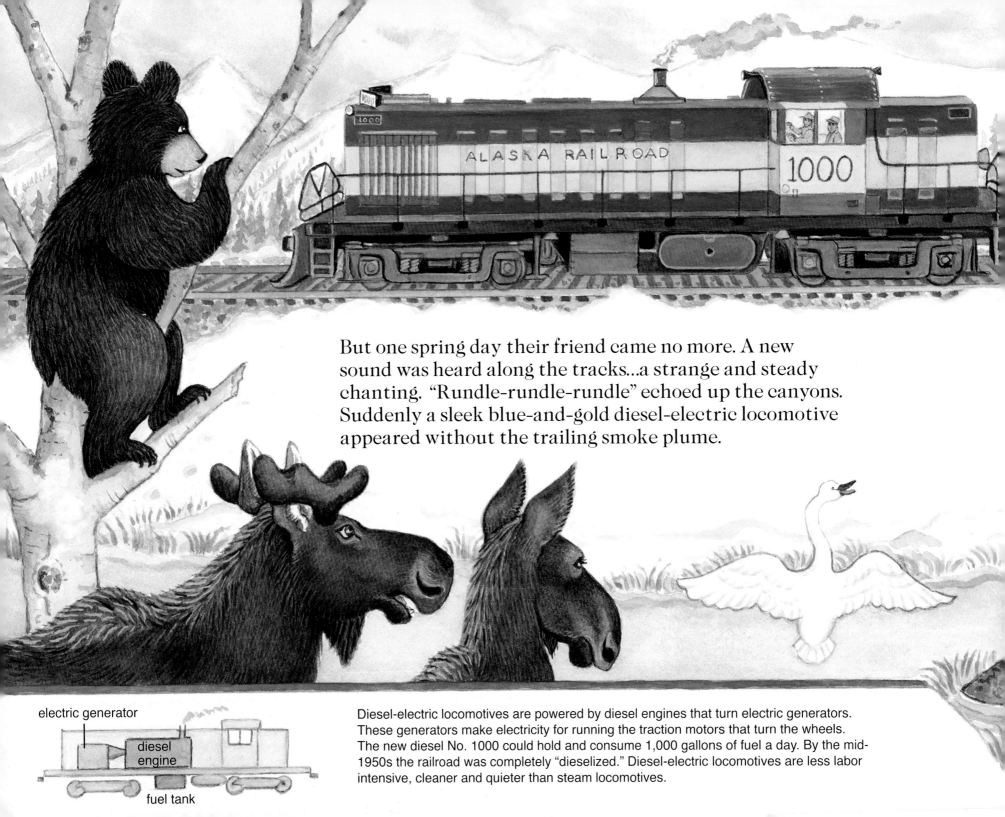

But one spring day their friend came no more. A new sound was heard along the tracks...a strange and steady chanting. "Rundle-rundle-rundle" echoed up the canyons. Suddenly a sleek blue-and-gold diesel-electric locomotive appeared without the trailing smoke plume.

electric generator

diesel engine

fuel tank

Diesel-electric locomotives are powered by diesel engines that turn electric generators. These generators make electricity for running the traction motors that turn the wheels. The new diesel No. 1000 could hold and consume 1,000 gallons of fuel a day. By the mid-1950s the railroad was completely "dieselized." Diesel-electric locomotives are less labor intensive, cleaner and quieter than steam locomotives.

He was in a hurry, not even stopping for a bite of coal or a drink of water. "That's the new Kid Diesel" cawed raven. "Humph! I think he's rude!" said moose.

13

Other changes were coming that bright spring morning. The sun had returned, bringing warmth to the Susitna Valley. Everywhere the snow was melting. Water dripped from the low branches of the spruce trees, gurgled down rocky gulches, laughed along the small streams and then joined the mighty Susitna River.

Beginning up river, the caribou heard it first and perked up their ears. It started so low they could scarcely hear..a little creaakk.. a low groan and grinding.. a rumble, then a long ccrr-a-a-a-ck... Roar!... CHAOS!... BREAKUP!... WAHOOOOOo!

14

The big Susitna River, swelling with the spring runoff, awoke from a long winter's nap. Huge blocks of ice spun into the current. Rushing and rollicking, they raced each other down river.

Suddenly the channel narrowed... SCRUNCH!

The ice blocks got stuck, then piled up! ICE JAM!

Then the water backed up behind the ice dam, flooded over the banks and across the tracks that ran beside the river.

Meanwhile, The Kid, his sides gleaming in the sun, was heading north fully loaded with passengers after a night's rest at the Curry Hotel. Rounding a sharp curve, he found himself in the rapidly rising flood waters.

Oh, no! The Kid did not like water! It shorted out his electric motors. With fuses popping, he slowly came to a sputtering stop in a shower of muddy spray.

Traction motors, which turn the diesel locomotive's wheels, are found underneath, between the wheels and very close to the rails. They won't run in more than 3 inches of water above the rail.

16

As the swirling river surrounded the stranded train, the passengers exchanged worried glances. The conductor made a call for help. "There's a flood on the Su... it's over the tracks, rising fast and we're unable to move!"

There were no communication radios until the 1950s; prior to that, crews used hand signals. Telephones were installed at the section houses, but if a call needed to be made in between them, a trainman used a "copper" to connect his phone to one of the telephone wires along the rail by using a long pole. This would connect him to the Anchorage train dispatcher who kept track of all crews and trains along the line.

17

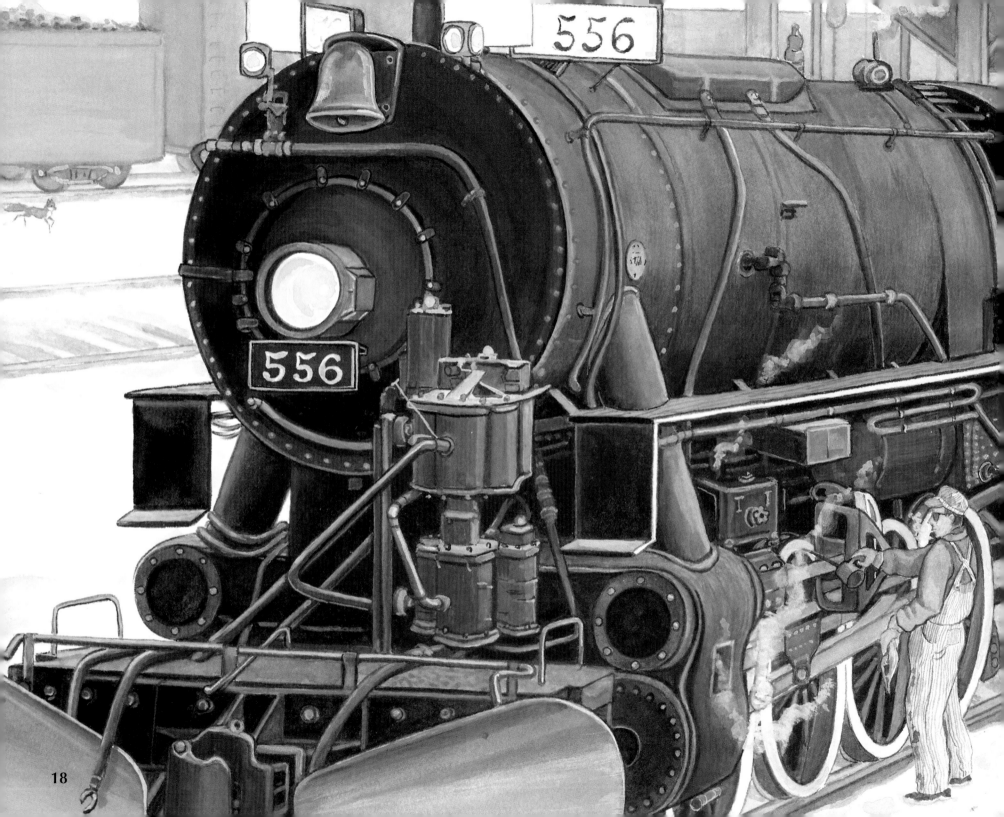

18

The call went out to the far north station where Ol' 556 was on standby, waiting for work. "There's trouble down the line... we need to highball south!"

Steve the conductor, Sparky the fireman and Wild Bill the engineer worked together as a team, loading coal and water into the tender, making sure Ol' 556 was greased up, steamed up and ready to go.

The conductor is in charge of the train and confirms the orders for the train crews. The engineer runs the locomotive and the fireman assists the engineer. In the steam days, the fireman kept up the steam production. He had to shovel coal constantly on steep grades when the train was carrying a heavy load. If he didn't keep up, the train would lose power. There usually is a brakeman on the train to assist the conductor.

White flags on the front of the engine signaled that the train was on an extra run—not a regular schedule. Two white lights were used when it was dark.

A "highball" is a fast departure on a clear track for a run at maximum, safe speed.

"Highball!" echoed Steve's call. Sparky shoveled coal into the glowing firebox.

Wild Bill cracked the throttle. Clang! Clang! WuuOO! WuuOO! Chisss... chisss! Chuuug... chuug!

Out of the siding and onto the main line, Ol' 556 was back in business with a big job to do.

The fireman and engineer had to wear goggles, heavily starched clothes, a handkerchief around their necks and their pant legs over heavy boots to shed cinders and to keep the heat off their skin in warm and cold weather. "In the summer you roasted; in the winter you froze, especially at 50° below!" Their heavily starched hats protected their heads from bumps in the small cab.

At times the steam engine's cab was so full of smoke, cinders and blowing snow that the engineer and fireman could barely see. There were canvas curtains that could be pulled to cover the top and side openings between the engine and tender to keep out bad weather.

21

Clickety-clack through the tunnels. Clickety-clack over the bridges along Nenana Canyon... steel wheels screeching on steel rails around the curves. Past McKinley... Windy... Cantwell... a stop at the top of Broad Pass for a quick drink from the water tower... Colorado, Honolulu... the section houses streamed past... over Hurricane Gulch... down Indian River canyon, heading south.

22

MCKINLEY PARK

WINDY

CANTWELL

BROAD PASS

COLORADO

Maximum speed for the steam engines was about 55 mph, but because of the poor condition of the tracks, they averaged 25-35 mph and took a day to get from Seward to Anchorage plus another three days to get to Fairbanks. With a major track improvement program, which was completed in 1952, and the new diesels on line, the three-day trip was cut down to one day. Today, Alaska Railroad trains travel up to 65 mph.

Wild Bill was on the alert for dangers. What's that lurking around the next bend? Boulders on the tracks? Mudslide? Avalanche? No, it was a herd of lazy moose enjoying the spring sun that brought them to a halt that day.

WuuOO! WuuOO! WuuOO! whistled Ol' 556. The moose recognized their old friend and stepped aside to let her pass. Wild Bill dropped sand for traction, then reached for the throttle. Ol' 556 surged ahead. She had never gone so fast!

The ARR has to be prepared for deep snow, avalanches, rockslides, ice buildup, frost heaves (that bind and buckle the tracks), and moose on the rails. A collision with a moose can derail a train. In the 1940s, one train was stuck in deep snow for 17 days. The crew cut firewood and melted snow to keep the engine fire going and steam circulating.

A wolf pack welcomed Ol' 556 as she thundered into view. They howled a greeting and raced along beside her. Up on the hillside, some bears ambled out of their den to watch Wild Bill cautiously driving Ol' 556 into the flood.

Steve waved her on... one foot, two feet and then three feet deep, almost to the top of her big driving wheels. Ol' 556 didn't mind the cold water as long as it stayed out of her fire box.

Steam engines can go through four feet of water; anything deeper would put out their fire.

The passengers, crowding at the windows and doorways, cheered as Ol' 556 came nose to nose with a very humble Kid. "Let's get you out—water's rising fast—no time to lose!" yelled Steve.

LROAD

556

The fireman had to always be checking the fire for cold spots, and clear out the clinkers, big unburned cinders that could smother the fire and slow the engine. He had to throw the coal where the fire was white—the hottest part.

The two engines were coupled. Clang! Clang! Wuoo! Wuoo! Wuoo! Chiss... chisss! Chuuug-chuug-chug! "Pour on the coal!" Sparky shoveled till his arms ached. Wild Bill threw Ol' 556 into reverse and opened the throttle. Steam billowed, blocking out the sun. Ol' 556 pulled with all her might!

Very slowly, Ol' 556 backed up, hissing and puffing, foaming and bubbling, working harder than ever before, pushing aside the slush and ice, pulling The Kid and his thankful passengers from the angry waters.

Everyone breathed a sigh of relief. Wild Bill hollered, "We did it!" and threw his sooty hat into the air!

And then came a crack like dynamite and a cascading ROAR!

The Susitna broke through the ice jam! Huge blocks of ice shot into the air, scraping against trees and rails. Then all was swept south in the raging river.

Drums of burning charcoal are still used in the winter to melt natural springs that glaciate over the tracks.

32

Ol' 556 had saved the day. She towed The Kid to the next section house to rest and dry out. Then she proudly pulled his weary passengers north to the McKinley Park Hotel for a hot meal and warm beds.

The tracks were repaired and the wildlife got used to the blue-and-gold trains streaking by (although moose never really did like them).

35

For many years, Ol' 556 was used to pull diesels through floods. When her working days finally ended, she came to rest at a park in downtown Anchorage for all to enjoy.

You can climb high up into her cab, feel the heat of Sparky's fire and hear Steve call "Highball!" Pretend you're Wild Bill, sooty engineer's cap on your head, hand on the throttle, and feel the big wheels slowly turning as Ol' 556 starts another journey north.

Now just watch out for those grumpy moose!

Photos by Wendy Reeves Spencer

The Engines

On a straight level track, the No. 556 could pull an average of 1,500 tons. In this photo, the No. 556 is pulling a train through a spring flood at Nenana.

The No. 556, an S-160 class locomotive, was one of 2,300 locomotives built for the U. S. Army in 1944. They lack the typical steam engine domes because many were sent to Europe where the bridges and tunnels were a lot lower than in America. Their short driving wheels meant they had a lot of pulling power but not much speed. They also had good traction on steep mountain grades.

Alaska Railroad Collection / Anchorage Museum at Rasmuson Center

The No. 1000, a 1,000-horsepower diesel-electric engine, could pull an average of 1,800 tons on a straight level track. In this photo, the front bar was used to break icicles in the tunnels leading to Whittier. Later, the crew cab was moved to the front of the locomotives where the crew got a better view.

The first diesel-electric locomotive, No. 1000, is on display north of Wasilla at the Museum of Alaska Transportation and Industry.

William Gibson / Pat Durand

Today, the No. 4000 series diesel electric locomotive, also known as "Mac," has 4,000 horsepower and is made by GM. It has a fuel capacity of 5,000 gallons and is very fuel efficient. It can pull about 4,000 tons on a level track. The tonnage goes down with the grade.

These trains usually include four diesel-electric locomotives and 80-to 90 freight cars that can stretch up to a mile long. One or two of the locomotives are sometimes used at the end of the train. Run by remote control, they push the load.

Randy Thompson

Fireman Bob Barnett (1934).

Alaska railroaders (mid 1920s). Engineer E. W. Barnett is on the far right.

Engineer Ray Gaylor (1948).

The real Wild Bill, engineer William T. Stewart (1945).

Pat Durand explaining the workings of No. 556.

Railroad maintenance workers near Cantwell (1939).

The Railroad

Cat train (1917) hauling supplies on a winter trail along the right-of-way prior to the construction of the Alaska Railroad.

A builder's photo of No. 701 at the Baldwin Locomotive Works in Philadelphia (1926). The steam locomotives were tested here and then disassembled before shipment to the Alaska Railroad because there were no cranes or barge service in Alaska at that time. The engines were reassembled in the Anchorage railroad shop which took four-to six weeks.

Train taking on passengers from the steamship *Admiral Watson* at the Anchorage railroad dock (1921).

The first engine to run on the Alaska Railroad (1917). Brand new, it had yet to get its No. 1 painted on the side.

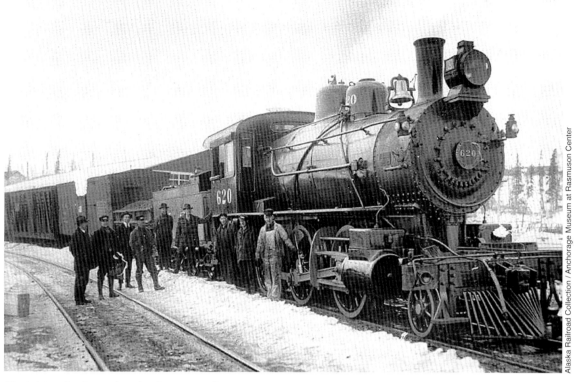

Freight train departing Anchorage railroad yard (1922).

Moose have always enjoyed traveling and resting along the railroad where the snow isn't so deep. (1930s)

Engineer Wayne Ware and Engine No. 312 (1945).

The tallest bridge on the Alaska Railroad in The Loop District between Seward and Anchorage (1918).

MATANUSKA WATER TANK. APRIL 14-1919.

Passenger train crossing the Matanuska River (1935).

Water tower near Palmer (1919). Note the smoke stack at the top. A small coal fired boiler at the base kept it from freezing in winter.

ALASKA
McKINLEY
NATIONAL PARK
ROUTE
RAILROAD

Steam meets diesel-electric in Whittier (1944).

No. 902 with passenger train at the Anchorage depot ready for its first in-service trip (1944). *Left to right,* hostler Al Robinson, engineer Charlie Diamond, conductor Norman Russell, general shop foreman Harry Doubt, Ray Bedford representing Baldwin Locomotive Works, and road foreman of engines E. W. Barnett.

"The Kid" finally arrives in Fairbanks (1948).

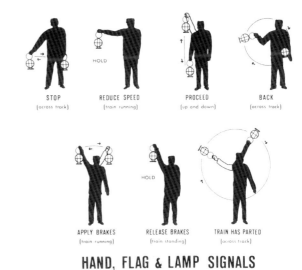

STOP
(across track)

REDUCE SPEED
(train running)

PROCEED
(up and down)

BACK
(across track)

APPLY BRAKES
(train running)

RELEASE BRAKES
(train standing)

TRAIN HAS PARTED
(across track)

HAND, FLAG & LAMP SIGNALS

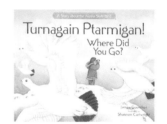

Tim Huffman

Shannon Cartwright came to Alaska 35 years ago after graduating from the University of Michigan School of Architecture and Design. For the past 30 years, she has lived in her remote home with her husband and two dogs up the Susitna River Valley with access via the ARR. Since that move, she has wanted to write and illustrate a train book. After many years of research and interviews with the railroad workers, Ol' 556 came to be. Shannon expresses her love of Alaska through the 26 books she has illustrated, four of which she has also written.

Shannon's books, prints and notecards can be obtained from:

Taku Graphics
5763 Glacier Highway
Juneau, AK 99801
(800) 278-3291
www.takugraphics.com